2 - 3

Lazy Circles

KEYS TO READING

a hawk makin' lazy

circles in the sky

OSCAR HAMMERSTEIN II

Louise Matteoni

Wilson H. Lane

Floyd Sucher

Versie G. Burns

Theodore L. Harris, *Advisory Author*

Harold B. Allen, *Linguistic Consultant*

THE ECONOMY COMPANY   Oklahoma City   Indianapolis   Orange, CA

Design: James Stockton

Cover Illustration: Jon Goodell

Permission to use or adapt copyrighted material appearing in
this book is gratefully acknowledged on pages 255-256, which
are hereby made a part of this copyright page.

ISBN 0-8332-1258-3

THE ECONOMY COMPANY, Educational Publishers
1901 North Walnut   Oklahoma City, Oklahoma 73125

Contents

A GOLD STAR

NOW THAT'S A GREAT IDEA

WHERE IN THE WORLD . . . ?

SHHHHHH!

Which Yellow Brick Road?

Runaway Tillie

We work with words.

believe	field	babies	stories
glad	glance	glue	
we're	they're		

bandit	pasture	whisper

purr	her	third	turn
anthill	birdseed	afternoon	

Sound the words.

Tillie

gloomy

you're

zookeeper

chimpanzee

hospital

surprised

runaway

Sight words.

The children gave Tillie an <u>orange</u>.

All at <u>once</u> the class got very <u>calm</u>.

7

Tillie lived at the zoo. One day
Tillie didn't get up to play. She
wanted to stay on her bed. So the
zookeeper had to call the doctor.

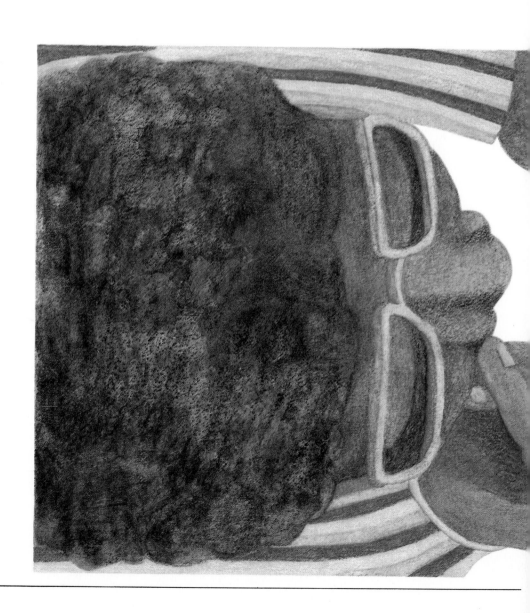

The doctor came. He found the little chimpanzee in bed. He looked at her.

"You're so gloomy!" he said. "Are you sick, Tillie?"

Tillie was very still. The doctor wanted to see what was wrong.

"I can't tell what is wrong," he said.
"We must take Tillie to an animal
hospital at once."

"O.K.," said the zookeeper. He took
Tillie to the car. She was very calm all
the way to the hospital.

They took her to a room in the
hospital. Then the doctor and the
zookeeper left. Tillie watched them go.
Now she was all alone. Tillie was afraid.
She wanted to get out of there!

The little chimpanzee jumped to the floor. Then she ran out the door. Soon she began to feel better.

She went into the room next door. Tillie was surprised! There were dogs all around her! And they all looked gloomy.

How surprised the dogs were to see Tillie! She went up to one dog. He gave a bark. Then he ran around and around. Tillie wanted to help. So she let the dog out.

All the dogs began to bark and bark. So Tillie let all of them out. The dogs jumped to the floor. They ran after her.

The zookeeper heard the noise. "Come back, Tillie!" he said. But Tillie ran on. She wanted to get away from the dogs. She was afraid.

All at once Tillie saw an open window. She didn't feel gloomy now. So out the window she went!

Tillie ran away from the hospital.
Soon she came to a school. She found an
open door. So she went in and looked
around. Soon she came to a class of
children. The teacher was not there.

"Look! A chimpanzee!" said a girl.
The surprised class began to talk to
Tillie. So she went into the room. She
picked up a stick. Then she jumped up
and down.

This was more fun than the hospital!

"Let's give that runaway chimpanzee something to eat," said a boy. And he gave Tillie an apple and an orange.

Other children in the class gave her food. Soon Tillie began to feel even better.

"Say, let's make the chimpanzee our pet," said a girl.

"O.K.! Let's do," said the class. "A class pet would be fun to have."

All at once the room was calm. The class sat down. A teacher was at the door. Tillie looked at the teacher. She put down her apple and orange. Tillie wanted to get back to the zoo!

So the runaway chimpanzee jumped out the window. She ran and ran. She ran into a man.

"Tillie! Come back!" said the man.

It was the zookeeper! Tillie came to a stop. The zookeeper picked her up. Tillie was very happy now.

"I found you, Runaway Tillie!" said the zookeeper. "I don't think you're sick at all. You're going back to the zoo!"

Mother Skunk's Moving Day

We work with words.

magazine   marine

place   choice   face   decide

cities   studies   carries

farmer   worker   killer

think   bank   trunk

night   fight   sigh

I'll   he's   it's

animal   family   fossils

Sound the words.

police

voice

babies

driver

skunk

highway

who's

officer

Sight word.

A <u>photo</u> of the skunk was in the paper.

17

Mother Skunk sat and looked at her new babies.

"Our family must have a new home," she told Father Skunk. "The people in the big house saw you last night. So we can't stay here anymore."

"I heard a voice say that skunk pelts sell for a lot of money," said Father Skunk. "We must go before we are found."

"Then let's not wait. Let's get moving now!" said Mother Skunk.

"Where will our new home be?" said
Father Skunk.

"I have found a place," said Mother
Skunk. "It's in the woods. And it's
across the highway."

"Who's going to move our babies to
the woods?" Father Skunk said.

"I will move them," said Mother Skunk.

Mother Skunk didn't rest that day.
Mother Skunk had to work all day on the
new home in the woods. She made a hole
by a tree. Then she put some leaves in
it. At last she could go back to move
her family.

One by one, Mother Skunk took her
babies to the road. Father Skunk waited
by the road with them.

Then Mother Skunk picked up one baby
in her mouth and went across the highway.

Just as she got out on the highway, two
cars came up.

Mother Skunk didn't stop, but the
cars did!

Mother Skunk hid one baby by the
road. Then she went back for the next one.

Soon, a lot of cars had to stop. "Who's
in our way?" said one driver in a gloomy
voice.

More and more cars had to stop. Then
a police car came up to the other cars.

"What is wrong here?" a police officer
said.

Then he saw Mother Skunk as she went across the highway. She had a baby in her mouth.

"Well, how about that!" said the police officer.

Then he went down the highway. The officer smiled. He said to each driver, "You will have to wait. A family is moving across the highway."

"Who's moving?" said a driver.

"Someone took a photo of the family," said the officer. "Just wait, and you'll see the story in the paper."

At last all the babies were across the highway. Then Father Skunk went across. The cars didn't have to wait anymore.

The next day people saw the story "Mother Skunk's Moving Day" in the paper. There was a photo of Mother Skunk with a baby in her mouth.

Think About This:

1. Where did the skunks move?
2. Why did the cars have to stop?
3. Why did the skunks have to move?

Mr. Ant and the Mistake _____

We work with words.

neighbor	eight	weigh
playing	trying	hurrying

lonely	likely	quickly
tried	fried	spied

looked   wanted

Sound the words.

neighbors

carrying

mailbox

suddenly

terrified

swayed

mistake

asked

Sight words.

"Don't hurt me, Mr. Giant," said George.

The giant thought about this.

One morning Mr. George I. Ant moved to a new town. But no one saw him move in. Everyone was still in bed.

It was not hard for Mr. Ant to find his new home. He had a wife and a lot of children. So he moved into the biggest home on the anthill.

"I'm going to paint my name on my mailbox," said Mr. Ant. "But there isn't room for all of it. I'll paint a **G** that stands for George and an **I** that stands for my other name. And then I'll paint my last name."

After a while Mr. Ant went for a walk. He was a nice ant who wanted to visit with his neighbors. But he could find no one.

"Where is everyone?" Mr. Ant thought. Then he went home and had dinner.

The next day, Mr. Ant went out for his morning walk. But the streets were still empty as he walked along.

"What is wrong?" he wondered.

The next day Mr. Ant ran all over the town. But again the streets were empty.

Suddenly Mr. Ant heard footsteps. Clump, clump, clump. The noise came from a long way away. Then the footsteps came closer and closer.

Mr. Ant waited. "Who can that be?" he wondered.

The footsteps went on and on. Clump! Clump! Clump! Mr. Ant was terrified!

Suddenly a big red ant came around the corner. He was carrying a club. It was so big that he swayed as he walked with it.

George I. Ant thought the red ant looked mean. But George I. Ant was too terrified to run. He just stood and shook.

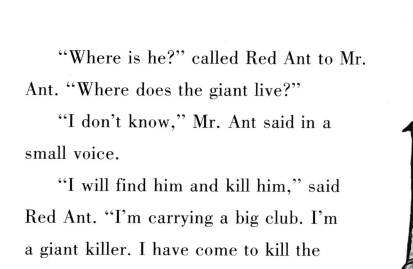

"Where is he?" called Red Ant to Mr. Ant. "Where does the giant live?"

"I don't know," Mr. Ant said in a small voice.

"I will find him and kill him," said Red Ant. "I'm carrying a big club. I'm a giant killer. I have come to kill the giant, but I won't hurt you."

"I'm happy about that!" called Mr. Ant.

"I must find that giant," Red Ant said as he shook his big club. "But he won't be hard to find. He has the biggest house in town."

"Oh, no!" said Mr. Ant. "It must be a mistake." But Red Ant didn't stop. He went on his way, carrying the club. Mr. Ant ran along behind him.

They came closer and closer to the biggest house on the anthill. "No giant lives there," Mr. Ant called out in a terrified voice.

"Yes, he does," said Red Ant.

The big red ant swayed as he went on up the street. Little Mr. Ant ran along behind him.

"Why do you think a giant lives there?" asked Mr. Ant.

"My neighbors told me he does," said Red Ant. "And they want me to kill him!"

"Oh, my! Oh, my!" said Mr. Ant. He was more and more terrified as they came closer to his anthill.

"See there?" said Red Ant. "He even has **GIANT** painted on his mailbox."

"Oh, no!" said Mr. Ant. "That is my house and my mailbox."

Red Ant looked at Mr. Ant with a mean look on his face. He shook his club at Mr. Ant.

"Wait!" Mr. Ant said suddenly. "I
made a little mistake. Now I will do
something about it. You wait and see.
All I need are two dots." Then Mr. Ant
ran inside for some paint.

Soon Mr. Ant came back to the mailbox.

He put two dots of paint in his name.
With the dots, it looked like this:

G.I.ANT

"That stands for my name—George I.
Ant," he said. "Now I know why our
neighbors went to hide. I know why they
wanted a giant killer. They thought I
was a giant."

"Well, you're sure not a giant," said Red Ant. "You're so small. Why do you live in an anthill this big?" he asked.

"My wife and all our children will be here this morning," Mr. Ant said. "Do you think the neighbors will come to visit now?"

"They will," said Red Ant. "It's a nice town. Still, it's too bad there isn't a giant!"

After that, Mr. Ant never made the same mistake. He always used George I. Ant when he had to give his name.

Think About This:

1. What was George I. Ant's mistake?
2. What parts of the story were make-believe?
3. What parts could really have happened?

Ants Live Here

Ants live here
by the curb stone,
see?
They worry a lot
about giants like
me.

by Lilian Moore

The Case of the Missing Dough

We work with words.

watching   jumping   making

word   world   worry

table   grumble   startle

Sound the words.

missing

worked

hung

arm

terrible

Miller

Sight words.

Gladys will change into a detective at night.

First, she answered the phone.

33

This is Baby Face Fred. He
likes dough. His friends call him the
Dough Boy. He doesn't seem to mind.

This is Detective Morris Russell.
His friends call him Irving. He does
seem to mind. He doesn't like Baby
Face.

This is Miss Miller. She's a friend of Detective Russell Morris. She's forever mixing up good things to eat.

Detective Morris Russell comes over to see her when he gets off work. He comes to tell Miss Miller about the case he has worked on all day. And he comes to lick the mixing bowl and eat good things. Miss Miller doesn't seem to mind.

Detective Russell Morris doesn't know that Miss Miller can change into . . . Fly-By-Night-Gladys!

Fly-By-Night-Gladys is better than the best detective. But Detective Morris Russell doesn't know that.

So now that you know all that, let's get on with things. Here is . . .

The Case of the Missing Dough.
Detective Russell Morris worked too hard. He wanted to take a day off. He wanted to go out and catch some fish. But, just as he was about to leave, he got a phone call. "Detective Morris Russell," he said.

"Help, Irving!" said a voice. "This is Oscar's Pie Place. Someone just made off with all of our dough."

"Did you get a good look at who it was?" asked Detective Russell Morris.

"Sure did. He had a baby face. And a black coat hung over one arm. He took all our pie and cake dough. And the gingerbread dough. Oh, it was terrible. Just terrible!"

"You just stay there," said Detective Morris Russell. "I'm coming over." He hung up the phone. "There goes my day off," he said. Just then he got another call. "Detective Russell Morris here."

"Irving? Herbert Street here. Help! All my cheese dough is missing! Someone took it!"

"Someone with a black coat hung over one arm?" asked Detective Morris Russell.

"How did you know?" asked Herbert Street.

"I have to know, I'm a detective. You just stay there, Herbert. I'm coming over," said Detective Russell Morris. He hung up the phone and took off. "So," he said to himself. "Baby Face Fred is up to his old tricks. Well, I know who did it. But, . . . where is he?"

Detective Morris Russell went by Miss Miller's to talk about the case. When he got there she was mixing up something good to eat. Detective Russell Morris took a lick out of the bowl. "It's . . . dough!"

An arm with a black coat hung over it
came out of the oven. Baby Face came
out with it. "Give me all that dough,"
he said.

"Baby Face Fred," said Detective
Morris Russell. "It's you!"

Baby Face laughed and took off out
the window with the dough. Fast!
Detective Russell Morris went after him.
Fast! But not as fast as Fly-By-Night-
Gladys!

Outside, Detective Morris Russell looked up. "It's a bird," he said. "No, it's a duck."

"No, it's really Fly-By-Night-Gladys," Baby Face called. "You won't get me, Gladys." And with that he tried to hide.

But Fly-By-Night-Gladys did get him!

"O.K., Baby Face," she said. "Come clean. Give me that dough. And why do you have that black coat hung over your arm?"

"Because I have no place to put it," said Baby Face.

Then Fly-By-Night-Gladys made him give back all the dough, and that was that.

Detective Russell Morris went back to Miss Miller's to tell her about the case. When he got there, she was mixing up something good to eat.

"Did you get Baby Face?" she asked.

"Oh, I had a little help from Fly-By-Night-Gladys," answered Detective Morris Russell. "But I got him."

"Well, good for you," said Miss Miller.

"You know," said Detective Russell Morris, "you should meet her. Fly-By-Night-Gladys, I mean. She's really something!"

Miss Miller smiled.

"Here, Irving," she said. "Why don't you just lick this nice mixing bowl?"

Bear Hugs

A Groundhog by the Fireplace

We work with words.

air   chair   pair

washcloth   herself   today

brother   ticket   dragon

plodded   biggest   gotten

three   thrill   throat

Sound the words.

upstairs

groundhog

fireplace

cricket

winter

hopped

throw

Roy Rabbit put on his red coat. Then he put on his shoes. He hopped down the road.

"Where are you going?" asked Sally Squirrel.

"I'm off to catch a cricket," answered Roy Rabbit. "Last winter I had bad luck. But this winter I'll have good luck. I'm going to put a cricket by the fireplace."

"If you ask me, crickets and good luck don't go together," said Sally Squirrel.

"Well, I'm going to catch a cricket!" said Roy Rabbit. And he hopped away.

Roy Rabbit found a snake. He found two bears, a fish, and a bat. He didn't find any crickets.

"That's bad!" said Roy Rabbit.

"What's bad?" asked a groundhog's deep voice. There by a tree sat Godfrey Groundhog.

"I can't catch a cricket," answered Roy Rabbit. "And I want one to sit by my fireplace. It brings good luck."

Godfrey Groundhog thought about this.
After a while he asked, "Do you know
that a groundhog by the fireplace brings
more good luck than a cricket? I'll be glad
to sit by your fireplace."

"Thanks, Godfrey," said Roy.

Roy Rabbit went home. On the way, he
saw Sally Squirrel. He told her that Godfrey
Groundhog would bring good luck.

"If you ask me, good luck and a
groundhog don't go together," said Sally.

"Thanks. But I'll try Godfrey Groundhog
and see," said Roy.

Roy Rabbit went on home. Then he got his dinner ready.

"Get some for me!" said Godfrey Groundhog.

"Don't you just sit by the fireplace? A cricket does," said Roy Rabbit.

"Oh, no! A groundhog must eat every day," answered Godfrey Groundhog.

The groundhog ate and ate and ate. There was only a little food for Roy Rabbit.

"If a groundhog brings good luck, I'll be glad to have a small dinner," thought Roy.

Then Roy Rabbit hopped over to sit by the fire. But the groundhog was sitting in Roy Rabbit's big rocking chair.

"That's my chair!" said Roy Rabbit. "Won't you sit in that little chair by the fireplace? A cricket would."

"Every groundhog must have a nice big chair," said Godfrey Groundhog. And he went on rocking in the chair.

So Mr. Rabbit sat in the little chair.

After a while Roy Rabbit went upstairs to go to bed. Godfrey Groundhog came upstairs, too.

"Don't you sleep by the fireplace? A cricket does," said Roy Rabbit.

"No. It hurts a groundhog's back to sleep on the floor. I must have a nice big bed upstairs," answered Godfrey.

So Roy went to sleep on the floor that night.

"I'm cold. My back hurts. And I want more to eat!" thought Roy Rabbit the next morning. "But I don't mind. A groundhog should bring me good luck!"

Days went by. Winter came. Godfrey Groundhog got fat. Roy Rabbit got thin and sad.

Every day Roy Rabbit said, "I don't want any more luck, Godfrey Groundhog."

But Godfrey Groundhog went on sitting and rocking by the fireplace.

One day a very thin and sad Roy Rabbit went to see Sally Squirrel.

"If you ask me," said Sally Squirrel, "I don't think a groundhog and good luck go together."

"That's true," said Roy Rabbit. "My back hurts and I am hungry. But is there any way to make him leave?"

"You should throw him out of the house like you would a cricket. I'll be glad to help," said Sally Squirrel. "Let's go to your house."

They went to Roy Rabbit's house. The fat groundhog was sitting by the fireplace.

"If he were a little cricket, we could throw him out of the house," said Roy Rabbit.

"We can't throw him. He's too fat.
But we can pick him up," said Sally
Squirrel. Roy Rabbit and Sally Squirrel
picked up Godfrey Groundhog. And
together they took him out of the house.

"Thanks for the help, Sally," said
Roy. "Now I won't have to be so thin.
The groundhog wasn't good luck for me.
But it's good luck for me to have you for
a friend."

"If you ask me, good luck and friends
go together!" said Sally Squirrel. "After
all, what's a friend for?"

A Bath for Gail Goose

We work with words.

caught   laughter

night   light   high

war   warn   ward

little   sizzle   middle

liked   coming   freezing

want   washing   waddle

Sight word.

It had <u>been</u> there a long time.

Sound the words.

laugh

funny

right

warm

kettle

sizzling

washcloth

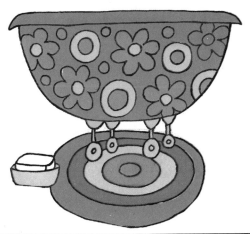

It was a warm day. Gail Goose said to herself, "I think I'll take a nice bath. I'll use my little green tub. I don't like water as well as my friends, Three-Ducks. But today is such a nice summer day. I'm going to take a good bath. I want to get all clean."

Gail Goose walked over to her little green tub. She filled the kettle with water. Then she plopped it on the stove to get it sizzling hot. Next she put some soap beside the tub.

"Now I'll read my newspaper while I wait for the water to get warm," said Gail Goose. "Then I'll take my bath."

After Gail Goose read one story, she thought, "My water must be warm now. It has been on the stove such a long time." So she went over to the tub.

"Oh," she said. "I forgot to get a washcloth."

So she got a blue washcloth. And she stuck it in the tub. She picked up the soap. Then she plopped into the tub herself.

"The soap is here. And the washcloth is here," she said to herself. "But this doesn't seem like a bath."

Gail Goose began to rub herself with the washcloth. "Soap, washcloth, me. Rub, rub! Soap, washcloth, me," she said. "But this doesn't seem like a bath."

Just then she heard her friends, Three-Ducks. They were quacking. She plopped out of the tub to see what the quacking was all about. She ran over to the window. And she stuck her long funny neck out.

"Three-Ducks!" she called. "Come and tell me what isn't right about my bath. Something just isn't right today."

Three-Ducks laughed. They said, "Maybe you forgot the soap."

Gail Goose looked around. "No, I have it," she said.

"What about a washcloth?" they asked.

Gail Goose looked around. "No," she said. "I have it. It's a blue one. Here it is."

"We will come in and look," said
Three-Ducks. And they did.

There was the little green tub.
Beside the tub was the washcloth.
Beside the washcloth was the soap. And
on the stove the sizzling kettle was
very warm.

Then Three-Ducks looked at Gail Goose.
They laughed. "We thought you were
funny," they said. "But we didn't know
you were as funny as that!"

"Well," said Gail Goose. "What isn't right about my bath today?"

Three-Ducks began quacking to each other. Then Three-Ducks laughed and laughed. They could only say, "The water, Gail Goose. You forgot the water!"

Gail Goose looked at the sizzling kettle on the stove. It was still filled with her bath water. She looked at the tub. It had not been filled with water. Then she began to laugh and laugh and laugh. "I thought there was something I didn't have," she said. "It didn't seem like a bath!"

The Popcorn Dragon

We work with words.

telephone   graph   photograph

germ   magic   ginger

unpack   untold   unwashed

also   already   altogether

Sound the words.

elephant

giraffe

unhappy

dragon

sighed

zebra

almost

sniff

Sight word.

<u>Dianne</u> was an unhappy dragon.

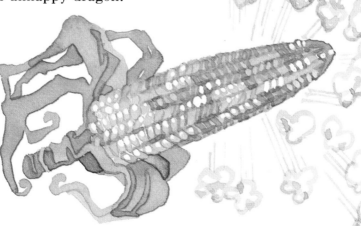

Dianne was a small green dragon. When she was unhappy, fire came out of her mouth.

One day Dianne had no one to play with. So she was unhappy. She sighed a deep sigh. But when she sighed, fire didn't come from her mouth. There were clouds of smoke!

"I'm blowing smoke!" said Dianne, and she ran to show her mother. "I didn't know I could do that," she told her. Then she blew more smoke.

"I'm going to show the other animals," she said. And off she trotted, blowing smoke all the way.

Soon Dianne came to the elephant, the giraffe, and the zebra. They saw her blow smoke. Their eyes almost popped out of their heads!

Suddenly the giraffe said, "Good-by, I have to go now." He slipped away and hid behind a rock. He tried to blow smoke like Dianne. But he couldn't do it.

Then the elephant said, "Good-by. I have to go." He trotted into the woods and tried to blow smoke like Dianne. But he couldn't blow smoke at all.

Then the zebra ran over a hill and tried to blow smoke. She tried and tried, but she couldn't do it.

After a while the zebra, the giraffe, and the elephant came back. They wanted to watch Dianne some more.

"I can blow smoke and you can't," Dianne said. And she trotted around, showing off.

"Now I think I'll blow smoke rings awhile!" said Dianne. She looked up in the air and blew smoke rings.

"Does Dianne really think she is funny?" asked the zebra.

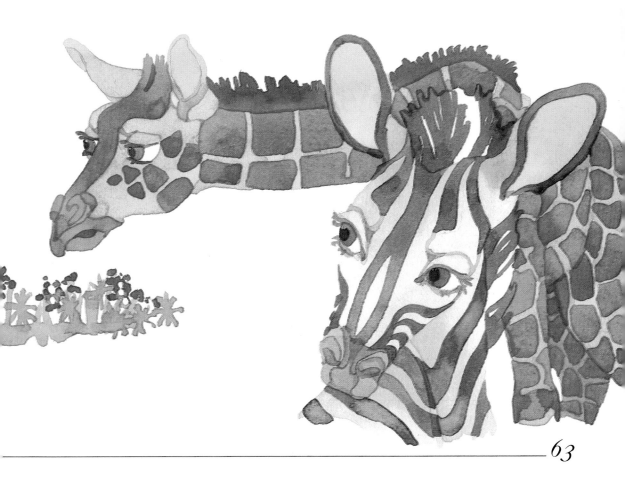

"We don't like her, do we?" asked the giraffe. The animals shook their heads.

"No, we don't! We don't like her one bit! She thinks she's so smart! Let's go!" said the elephant.

When Dianne saw the animals going, she didn't blow more smoke rings.

"Want me to come with you?" she called.

"No. We don't like to watch you show off," said the giraffe.

So Dianne sighed a big sigh of smoke and went home alone.

"Help me think of something to do," Dianne said to her mother.

"Blow some smoke," said her mother.

"I don't feel like it," said Dianne.

"Why not play awhile with the other animals?" said her mother.

"They won't play with me," said Dianne. She was very unhappy.

"I think you were showing off a bit," her mother said with a sigh.

Dianne was sorry about showing off, so she sat down to think about it awhile. She sat in a place where her friends grew corn. Soon she went to sleep.

After a long sleep, Dianne woke up to a funny popping noise. "Pop, pop! Pop, pop, pop!"

Something smelled good, too.

"Popcorn!" said Dianne. Fire had slipped out of her mouth. It had popped an ear of corn.

Dianne began to eat almost all the popcorn. Then she saw other ears of corn. So she blew on them and popped more popcorn. The smell of the popcorn was very good.

The giraffe, the zebra, and the
elephant heard the popping noise. They
put their heads up in the air and went
sniff, sniff, sniff. Then they came to see
what made the popping noise and what the
good smell was.

"Have some popcorn?" asked Dianne.
"You ate it all," said the zebra.
"I'll pop some more," said Dianne.
And she popped corn for all the animals.
"A dragon can be very nice when she
isn't showing off," said the giraffe. "Let's
ask Dianne to play with us."

Now Dianne would not show off. If she had to blow smoke, she moved away from everyone.

And when the animals were hungry, Dianne popped popcorn for everyone!

Think About This:

1. What happened to make Dianne a happy dragon?

2. What did Dianne learn about making friends?

The King and the Cook ____

We work with words.

thought	cough	bought
group	through	you
carry	arrow	marry

| larger | page | gentle |

Sound the words.

brought

soup

narrator

banish

magic

Sight words.

The <u>palace</u> was in the <u>country</u>.

<u>Alice</u> didn't want to be <u>quiet</u>.

Your class can put on the play *The King and the Cook* with very little trouble. You must have a place to put it on, and a cast. Then you must pretend.

All the people in the cast will stay
in the same spots as they put on the play.
They will dress the same as they do every
day. And your room will look the same
as it does every day.

That is why your class must pretend.
The cast must make everyone see a palace
even when it isn't there. The cast must
make everyone see a princess, a cook,
and a king even when they are just the
friends you see every day.

To do these these things, the cast must
read the play well. And the rest of the
class must try to see things that aren't
really there.

So just pretend, and have fun with
The King and the Cook.

Cast:

Jolly Jo

King

Maid

Princess Alice

Boy

Godfrey

Narrator

Scene 1

Narrator: It is day, and all is quiet in the palace of the king. Jolly Jo begins shouting.

Jolly Jo: Good day to you!

Maid: Quiet!

Jolly Jo: What went wrong? The palace was filled with happy noise this morning. Everyone sang and laughed. But now it's so quiet.

Boy: The king is eating his dinner. No one must say a word!

Maid: You must be very quiet. Not even
his friend, Godfrey, can say a word
when the king is eating.

Boy: Dinner must be just right or he will
get mad. Everyone must be quiet so the
king can think about his food.

Jolly Jo: What if he doesn't like it?

Maid: The king will get red in the face
and begin shouting, "Banish that cook
from the country!" Then the first cook
has to go away. The second cook will
then be the first cook. The third
cook will then be the second cook.
And a new third cook must be brought
to the palace. We have a lot of cooks
each week!

Boy: Everyone here has heard about the
king and the cooks. You must be new to
our country.

Jolly Jo: Yes, I'm new. I want to find
   work here. I'm a cook!
Narrator: Jolly Jo doesn't have time to
   say one more word. Suddenly shouting
   is heard.
King: The milk is hot! Banish that cook
   from the country!

Maid: Well, now! You can see we must have a new third cook. Go to the kitchen. I'm sure you can be a cook.

Boy: But it won't last long! No cook is here for more than a week.

Jolly Jo: Just wait and see!

Narrator: It is day, and Jolly Jo is working in the palace kitchen. Princess Alice is talking to him.

Princess Alice: That was a good story, Jolly Jo. It's nice that you brought magic stories to tell. I hope you can stay here for a long, long time.

Jolly Jo: I hope for the same thing.

Narrator: Suddenly Alice looks around.

Princess Alice: Look, they took dinner to Father!

Jolly Jo: Yes, the first cook made a vegetable soup.

Narrator: From the dining room they hear shouting.

King: This vegetable soup is too cold. Banish that cook!

Jolly Jo: Well! This is just my first day. And now I'm the second cook! Maybe I won't last long here after all.

Narrator: Jolly Jo is working in the palace kitchen as second cook while Princess Alice is talking to him.

Princess Alice: Did they take dinner to my father?

Jolly Jo: Yes, Princess.

Princess Alice: He better like it! I don't want you to be first cook. First cooks must go away.

Jolly Jo: Everything will be O.K., Princess. The king is eating his pie, and it's filled with fruit brought from a long way away. He should like it!

Narrator: Then from the dining room they hear the king shouting.

King: Banish that cook from the land! There is too little fruit in this pie!

Princess Alice: No, no! Now you are first cook, Jolly Jo! And soon you will have to go.

Jolly Jo: Don't cry, little princess! Magic can't work when you cry.

Princess Alice: Magic? What magic?

Jolly Jo: I cook with magic! And you must help me. What do you say?

Princess Alice: Oh, yes, Jolly Jo! I'll do everything you say.

We work with words.

lonely   badly   weekly

able   gentle   circle

Sound the words.

quickly

table

thirty

Scene 2

Narrator: The king is about to eat the first dinner cooked by Jolly Jo. He sniffs the food.

King: What can this be? It's brown and
   fresh, and it smells good! But how
   can I eat it if I don't know what it
   is?

Narrator: The king stands up, but again
   he sniffs the food. It smells so good
   that he quickly sits back down. He
   sniffs again.

King: Well, it won't hurt to take just
   one bite. Hmmm. It's crisp. I'll
   try some more. Hmmm. It sure is
   crisp.

Narrator: Soon all the food is gone. A
   boy quickly comes to the table.

King: I wish to see Godfrey.

Boy: I'll get him for you very quickly.

Godfrey: You called for me?

King: Yes, Godfrey. I don't know what
I had for dinner. But it was fresh
and crisp and good. The new cook
tried to play jokes on me and keep it
a secret. In the morning you will eat
with me. Together we can try out what
the new cook brings to my table. I
must count on you to help me.

Narrator: The next morning, Jolly Jo is
still first cook in the palace.

Princess Alice: I would not have
    believed it! Father ate with Godfrey
    today. They didn't know what they
    were eating, but both of them liked
    it. They both ate until all the food
    was gone. Now Father is going to
    have a lot of people to dinner. He
    used to eat alone. What is going on?

Jolly Jo: My magic is working!

Narrator: Three days have gone by.
Jolly Jo is still first cook.

Princess Alice: Jolly Jo! There are
thirty people dining with Father.

Jolly Jo: Yes, Princess. And there
were thirty dining this morning, too.

Princess Alice: But now I'll worry,
Jolly Jo. You put noodles in the
soup. Even now someone takes a
plum pie to put on the dining room
table. Father likes these foods. He'll
know if they are not cooked the way
he likes.

Jolly Jo: No, Princess. He won't know.
The king will be talking to his thirty
friends. He'll tell jokes until
everyone laughs. He won't worry about
the noodles or the plum pie.
He'll only know that the food smells
good, that his friends are happy, and
that his jokes are funny.

Princess Alice: I would not have believed it! Your magic is working! I knew I could count on you, Jolly Jo. Father will never again have time to worry about how the palace foods are cooked. Do you have some of your magic for me? Or must you keep it a secret?

Jolly Jo: It takes a little magic to
   cook, Princess. But I still have more
   magic. And now I'll have forever to
   tell you my magic stories!

A Friend Is...___

We work with words.

drive   drill   drop

Sound the words.

dream

A friend is someone to
see new things with.

A friend is someone to play with.

A friend is someone to read with.

A friend is someone to laugh with.

A friend is someone who is nice to you on
your birthday.

A friend can be someone in your family.

A friend is someone you can be happy with.

A friend is someone to love.

A friend is someone who
will read your new shirt.

A friend is someone
who cares for you.

A friend is someone to
dream with and to
dream about.

A Gold Star

Duchess

We work with words.

bush   put   pull

beauty   bandeau

Sound the words.

bushy

beautiful

entered

Duchess

Sight word.

The <u>lamb</u> couldn't get its foot out from under the rock.

One day Dad called from the door,
"Jeff, I have a surprise for you!"

"I'm coming, Dad," said Jeff. He
entered the house.

"A dog!" Jeff said, as he ran across
the room.

"I've found a new friend for you. Her
name is Duchess," said Dad.

The big brown and white dog wagged
her bushy tail. She walked closer to Jeff.

"Oh, she is beautiful, Dad!" said
Jeff. "I'll take good care of her. I've
wanted a dog for a long, long
time."

"Well, you know we have to think about Jill's sheep," said Dad. "So if Duchess can't get along with the sheep, we can't have her out here."

"I won't let her go anywhere close to Jill's sheep," said Jeff.

He began showing Duchess the house and the fields. They entered the barn and looked around. Then he took her down to the pasture gate.

Jeff went up to the gate. He said, "No, no," to Duchess. "You can go anywhere but this pasture." Duchess barked and wagged her tail. Jeff thought Duchess would stay away from the pasture gate.

After that, Duchess ran in the woods and across the fields. But she seemed to remember to stay away from the sheep pasture.

"I'm sure she'll remember," said Jeff.

One day it began to rain, so all the
family went to town. Duchess wanted to
go to sleep in the barn. Then she heard
a new noise. It was the cry of a sheep.

Duchess pushed open the barn door.
She ran down the hill and jumped over
the pasture gate. The noise was coming
from the end of the pasture.

Duchess came to a brook. The cry was
closer now. She ran by the brook until she
came to a rock pile. There was a little
lamb. Its foot was under a rock, and it
couldn't get out.

Duchess seemed to know what to do. She scratched at the rock and moved it away. Then the little lamb got its foot out.

Now other sheep were coming to the brook. Rain was still coming down, and the water was deep. Duchess seemed to know that she must keep the sheep away from deep water.

She went to the top of a rock and barked. The sheep ran close together. Then Duchess got behind them and barked. The sheep seemed to know what to do. They ran up the hill. Duchess ran along with them.

Then she heard someone calling. It was Jeff. He was on the hill with his family.

"Duchess! Why are you in the sheep pasture?" called Jeff.

Duchess put down her head and bushy tail. She walked close to the ground.

Then Jill saw the deep water. "Get those sheep up the hill, Duchess! Come on, all the way!" Jill called. "You have saved my sheep!"

Duchess barked at the sheep, and they came up to the gate.

"Beautiful Duchess, you saved the sheep!" said Jeff. "Jill, couldn't Duchess take care of them from now on?"

"That's O.K. with me!" said Jill.

Think About This:

1. What is another good name for this story?

2. How could Duchess help her family?

A Wild Goose Flying

We work with words.

guest guide guard

hidden taken written

beside because become

Sound the words.

guess

gotten

below

Down on Ice

Jim and Molly knew it had been cold during the night. It had gotten below freezing. They ran down to see the ice on the lake. Then Molly saw something white on the ice.

"Jim, come here," Molly called to her brother. "Look! Below that rock! A wild goose!"

"He's not dead, is he?" asked Jim. "I hope he's not dead."

"No, he's not dead, but he's hurt," said Molly. "And he's freezing out here. He needs help. Let's take him inside."

After they had gotten inside, Dad looked at the goose. "That's a snow goose," he said. "He was flying south for the winter with other geese. His wing is hurt and he needs food. But after the wing heals, he should be flying again."

Molly and Jim made a pen in the barn
for the goose. They put water and some
corn in the pen.

After a while, the goose began to eat
some corn. In a few days he was eating
all they put out for him.

"Just what do you think you'll do with
the goose?" Mother asked one day. "He
can't sit in that pen forever."

"I guess we'll let him fly south when
his wing heals," Jim said.

Mother shook her head. "His wing won't
be well for a long time," she said. "I don't
think he'll be flying south this winter."

"He needs to be with some other
geese," said Jim.

"After winter he could fly with the
other geese," said Mother. "But I don't
know what he would do after being in a
pen all winter."

"Let's keep him forever," said Molly.

"We don't own him, you know," said Mother.

"Why not?" asked Molly.

"The goose is a wild animal," Mother said. "And people don't own wild things."

Jim and Molly knew that no one could really own a wild goose. But they didn't know how to let the goose go free.

"You can take him to the big chicken pen," said Dad. "I guess the goose will be O.K. there. But maybe he won't be happy in a chicken pen."

"Why won't he be happy?" asked Jim.

Dad answered, "If you could fly up by the clouds, would you want to be free? Or would you want to be in a chicken pen?"

"I guess I would want to be free," Jim said. He watched the way the goose walked around inside the pen. He knew it wanted to be free.

"I know you'll want to fly when your wing heals," he said.

We work with words.

wrap   wreck   wrinkle

prince   dance   glance

Sound the words.

write

since

airline

Sight words.

A <u>ranger</u> brought boxes to the children.

The goose beat his <u>great</u> wings.

Flying South

One day Molly found a picture of a jet plane. Under the picture was FLY SOUTH FOR THE WINTER!

"Fly south for the winter!" Molly thought. "That's what our goose wants to do. I see him beat his great wings on the sides of the pen."

Then Molly ran to see Mother.
"Mother, would a jet take our goose south for the winter?" asked Molly.

"A jet plane?" asked Mother. Then she saw the picture. "Yes, if the goose were in a crate. But I think a crate would cost too much money."

"Can we find out how much it would cost?" asked Molly.

"We are too far away from an airline," said Mother. "We can't go that far."

"I'll write to an airline," said Molly.

"I guess you could do that," said Mother. "Get Jim. He can watch you."

So Jim and Molly got together to write to an airline. After a few days, a man came to see them. He had two boxes. "I'm a ranger," he said. "Did Jim and Molly write the airline? I have some boxes for them."

"Great! That's us!" said Jim.

"The airline wants to fly your goose
south — for free," said the ranger.

"Since you did so much and saved
the wild goose, the airline wants you to
have these boxes."

Molly looked at her gift. "Oh, I have
a picture of a great snow goose flying in
the sky," she said. "I can look at it and
remember how our snow goose looked."

"Well, I have something to help us remember how he went south," Jim said. He was showing a jet plane he had put together.

The ranger went to see the goose. He put a band around its leg. Then he put the goose inside a crate and made sure the sides were shut.

"Will the other geese be nice to him?" Molly asked. "Or will they be mean?"

The ranger laughed. "Because your goose rode so far in a plane?" he asked.

"No," Molly said. "They could be mean because he didn't fly south with them."

"Your goose will go south after the other geese. But the other geese will take him in. I put a band on his leg, so we'll know if we ever see him again."

Molly looked at her picture. "Maybe he'll fly back here," she said. "We'll watch for him."

"Maybe he'll remember us," said Jim. "Because we'll remember him!"

Tom Goldenrod

We work with words.

they   prey

nation   collection   invention

chief   piece   brownie

angry   hungry   finger

market   garden   large

Sound the words.

hey

reservation

bounced

Goldenrod

outfield

already

angrily

interested

charge

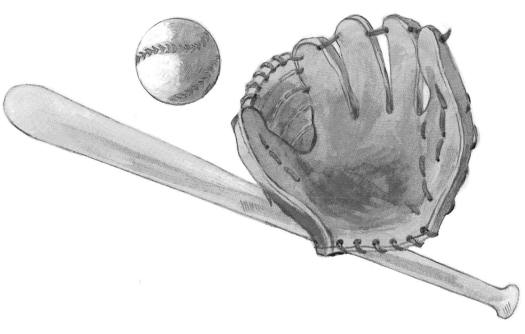

The ball bounced once and came right at Tom Goldenrod. He stood at third base and waited. He would let the ball come to him. But then it hit a small rock just before it got to him. It bounced into the outfield. Everyone on the Nelson team sighed.

"Throw it home!" they shouted to the left fielder.

But the game was already over. By the time the ball got to home plate, the Dogwood player was already there. Tom's team stood around him.

"Can't you even stop a grounder?" Alice asked angrily. She threw her hat down.

"Maybe that's how they play on the reservation," Russell said. "But if you want to keep on with Nelson, things better look up."

Tom got mad.

"I don't come from a reservation!" he said angrily.

Tom had lived in Nelson for only a few weeks when his father asked if Tom could play on the team. The coach wasn't interested in him at first. But he said he could use a good hitter for the game with Dogwood.

Suddenly there was a hand on Tom's back. It was the coach.

"Hey, Tom, what went wrong out there? Did you have something on your mind?"

"I wanted to wait," Tom said. "The ball was coming right at me. Then I don't know what went wrong—the ball just wasn't there anymore."

Tom looked around at the other people on his team. He could tell they were mad at him.

"I saw it all," Jennifer said. She walked over to the third-base line and picked up a small rock.

"The ball hit this and bounced off. No one could ever catch a ball like that."

"Why didn't you charge the ball?" Alice asked angrily. "You could have had it before it hit the rock."

"Tom's play was just right," Jennifer said, "because the ball was going too fast to charge it."

"Let's not get into it now," the coach said. "It's over. But in a few weeks we have one more game. If we beat Godfrey, we'll still be in first place."

"We can't beat them with him on our team," George said, as he looked at Tom.

"Yeah," Alice said, "he tries to play like he's got a bow and arrow in his glove."

Most of the team laughed and walked away.

Tom walked across the outfield to go home.

"Hey! Mind if I walk along with you?" Jennifer called, as she tried to catch Tom.

"Are you sure you want everyone to see you with me?"

"Look, we'll beat Godfrey and the team will forget about everything," said Jennifer.

"You think so?" Tom asked.

"Sure," said Jennifer.

Tom smiled. Then suddenly he said, "I could make a mistake again. Or . . ."

"Or you could help us beat Godfrey, Tom. After all, you're a good hitter," said Jennifer.

Jennifer wanted to talk about something other than the game. "How did your family get a name like Goldenrod?" she asked.

"My family used to live close to a field of goldenrods," Tom said as he came to his house. "So they took the name."

Both of them smiled.

"Well, rest up, and I'll see you at the game, Tom. I know everything will turn out great."

When Jennifer got home she tried to watch TV, but she wasn't interested in it. She thought and thought about Tom. She wanted to do something to help.

The sun was out the day of the big game. The Nelson team stood together in the center of the field with the coach.

"I want everyone to do well," the coach said. "And all I want to know is that you all will try as hard as you can. Right?"

"Right!" the team shouted.

The game started. For a while both teams made mistake after mistake. Then, at their last turn at bat, a Godfrey player made a home run. Nelson came up to bat with the team behind by one run.

Alice was first up. She hit a line drive. A Godfrey player tried to catch it, but the ball bounced out of his glove. Alice made it to second base.

The next player up to bat was Russell.

"Strike one, strike two, strike three," were called one right after the other.

Jennifer came up to bat next.

If she could hit a home run and bring Alice in, too, the game would be over. Nelson would beat Godfrey.

Jennifer watched the first ball go by. Then she looked over and saw Tom as he waited for his turn at bat. Right then it came to her. She had to give her friend a chance. She made wild tries at the next three balls, missing each one.

"You're out!" was barked in her ear.

"What went wrong?" the coach asked.

"I don't know," Jennifer said as she sat down. "He can throw fast balls."

Now it was Tom's turn. The first
ball went by, and then the second. But
on the third Tom hit a line drive into
the outfield. The Godfrey fielder didn't
have a chance.

The Nelson team went wild as Alice
ran for home plate. Tom threw off
his hat and ran by each base. First,
second, third. His team waited for
him at home plate. Jennifer watched
as her team walked off, carrying Tom
with them.

She heard Alice say, "I'm sorry about the bow-and-arrow jokes, Tom."

But Tom had already forgotten about the jokes. He was happy now. He was glad that Jennifer gave him a chance during the game. He knew that she didn't ever strike out. She had done that so he could win the game for Nelson.

"Coach, I'm sorry about the Dogwood game," said Tom.

"That's over and forgotten now, Tom," said the coach.

Tom and Jennifer just looked at each other and smiled.

Now That's a Great Idea

Mr. McBean's Train

We work with words.

largest   smallest   highest

fence   chance   sense

Sound the words.

longest

bedroom

else

button

Sight words.

Mr. McBean was building a big train.

Your train says, "Who-ohh," said Mrs.

McBean.

For days Mr. McBean did not feel well. So one morning he went to see his doctor.

"Mr. McBean, it's time for you to slow down," said the doctor. "You must stop building large things. Think about building smaller things. Then you'll get well."

"Oh, my!" moaned Mr. McBean. He left the doctor and went home.

"The doctor said I must stop building large things. I must get to work on some smaller things!" cried Mr. McBean from his living room.

"What smaller things?" asked his wife.

"We must find some little things for me to do," said Mr. McBean. "This will help me to slow down."

"Let's go upstairs and find little things you can do," said Mr. McBean's wife.

"Good, good!" cried Mr. McBean. And
he ran up the stairs to the top floor, where
there was a large trunk.

"I found something!" said Mr. McBean.
"Here's a little old train in this trunk. I'll
make it the biggest and longest train of all!"

"The biggest! The longest!" cried
Mrs. McBean. "Now, you know the doctor
said to work with little things."

But Mr. McBean had not heard his wife. He was building the longest train track he had ever seen. And he liked to make it longer and longer.

Soon the track ran all over the house. It ran into the living room, the bedroom, and the kitchen, and up and down the stairs.

Then little Mr. McBean went to the bedroom. He ran the train from his bed. He made it stop and go. And he made the train go who-ohh, who-ohh!

"Now there is nothing else for me to do," moaned Mr. McBean.

"Run the train!" said Mr. McBean's wife.

"It's no fun now," moaned Mr. McBean. "I must get up and make a longer track."

"No," said Mrs. McBean. "The doctor said you'll have to slow down and think about little things."

Mrs. McBean went to the kitchen. "Oh!" she said. "Here's something else we can do with the train."

Mrs. McBean wrote a note. She put it on the train. The note said, "Would you like some milk?"

The little train left the kitchen and took the note around the living room and up to the bedroom. "Who-ohh, who-ohh," went the train.

Mr. McBean saw the note. Then he wrote a note to his wife. It said, "Yes, I would like some milk, and some cake, too." He pushed a button.

Now there was something else to do with the little train!

One morning the doctor came to see Mr. McBean.

"Hello, Doctor," said Mr. McBean. "I'm building little things. Sit down, and you'll see."

Mr. McBean wrote a note. Then he pushed a button. The doctor watched the train come up the track.

Mr. McBean put the note on the train and pushed the button again. The train left.

The doctor laughed and laughed when Mr. McBean's train came back with milk and cake.

"Soon I'll be well!" said Mr. McBean to the doctor. "And here's some milk and cake for you!"

Think About This:

1. Why did the doctor tell Mr. McBean to do little things?
2. Would you like to have a train like Mr. McBean's train? Why?

From Horse to Helicopter ____

We work with words.

Sound the words.

high-heeled

ranch

cattle

market

carried

helicopter

hear   clear   learn   wears

Sight word.

<u>Machines</u> help the ranch hands do their work.

A ranch hand had to work hard a long time ago. On a big ranch he might work alone for days. He might not get much food or sleep for weeks at a time.

The ranch hand didn't work inside. So he had a big hat to keep the sun and rain off his face. And he used his high-heeled boots to help him get on or off his horse.

A ranch hand had to have a horse. He rode for days on a cattle drive. It took weeks to get them to market.

There were times when there was more than one ranch hand to do the work.

A chuck wagon went with the ranch hands on a cattle drive. The chuck wagon carried food for the ranch hands.

Today things have changed for the ranch hand. Machines help with the work.

Now a ranch hand can drive a jeep or even fly a helicopter as he works. In a jeep he can get around the ranch faster than on a horse. He can get all the cattle together from a helicopter. Then the cattle can be carried to market by train or by truck. Today a fast truck is used for a chuck wagon on the cattle drive.

Now it doesn't take much time to do work that took weeks to do in the old days.

So the cattle get to market faster.

Some things have not changed for
the ranch hand. He still rides a horse
some of the time. And he still rides
and works out in the sun and rain. So
he wears a big hat just like the
ranch hands of long ago. He wears
high-heeled boots, too. The cattle
drive and roping cattle are parts of
his work even today. A ranch hand still
has to work very hard. But machines
like the jeep, the truck, and the
helicopter have changed his way of
working.

The ranch hand has come a long way
from horse to helicopter.

The Neverset Invention

We work with words.

motion   auction   fraction

ice   circus   saucer

boxcar   railroad   somewhere

Sound the words.

invention

Janie

decided

neverset

Sight word.

Janie nailed the cards on the <u>board</u>.

Come in, Janie

One thing about my father is that he has this thing about the dark. He doesn't think I should be out in it.

As soon as the sun goes behind the Banners' roof, he sticks his head out the door. He calls, "Janie, you come on in now."

I told Pat and Sam, "I can't stand it. Why do I have to go in the second it's dark? Your fathers let you stay out until after dark."

Their fathers don't stick their heads out the door and call for them as if they are babies and must go to bed.

"Janie!"

"I have to go," I said.

That night I decided I had to do
something about it. I could still hear
the other kids. They were about to play
kick-the-can. The best time to play
kick-the-can is after dark.

I thought for a long time as I sat up
in bed. After a while I decided to make
a "neverset" invention that could make
the sun stay up all night.

I waited until everyone went to sleep.
Then I got together everything that was
on my list. I worked a long time on it.
Here is what my list looked like:

Invention list:
one board
some big nails
some little nails
one tin can that used
to have peaches
in it
my old yellow and
green shirt
three baseball cards
one golf ball
painted yellow, by hand

When I had all this in one place, I
threw my yellow baseball shirt over it.
I put it in the back corner of my closet.
Then I fell into bed.

When Pat and Sam came out the
next morning they said, "Hey." I said,
"Hey." We decided to throw the ball
around. Then we went to the lot across
the street and made a house out of old
things we found. Next we sat in the
house and played a game with sticks and
rocks.

Pat said to me, "You're quiet today. What's wrong?"

"I want to tell you, but I can't," I said.

"Is it a secret?"

"It's top secret."

"Who is it about?"

"Me."

Sam said, "Oh, well then, if it's about you, you can tell it."

So what could it hurt? I told them.

Sam laughed. Pat laughed, too.

I stood up. "It's not funny," I said.

"You can't make an invention like that," Sam said.

"You'll see," I said. "When the sun goes down in the sky, Neverset will keep it up. Just be here right before dark."

I went into the house and ate a lot of popcorn. That made me feel better, but I couldn't sit still.

Just a little while before dark, Sam and Pat knocked on the door and I let them in. I had everything ready. Were they surprised when they saw it!

I put the yellow golf ball into the tin can. I put my old shirt over it. Then I nailed the shirt down to the board with the big nails. Next I nailed the baseball cards on the board with the little nails.

Sam and Pat tried to ask how my
Neverset invention worked. I never
answered. A person doesn't have to tell
everything about her invention.

At last I nailed all the nails into
the board.

"Now what?" Pat asked me.

"Now nothing. Nothing at all." I said
this in a very funny voice. And I made my
eyes as little as I could make them.

We work with words.

pulling running stopping

crawl lawn because

Sound the words.

stickball

getting

yawning

Sight words.

Sarah used the pliers to get the nail out of the board.

It Works!

We all went out and played stickball until dinner time. My father called me in for dinner. I ate, then went back out again after some of us did the dishes, and some of us didn't.

We played stickball some more. Then we had a race. George fell and hurt his arm and had to go in.

Then we each rode my new bike until everyone got tired of that. It was time for red light-green light. We played that until everyone got mad because there was too much shouting.

"You moved!" and "No, I didn't!" and "You looked!" and "No, I didn't!"

So someone said, "Let's play kick-the-can." Someone else said, "It's not dark out here." So everyone made up and we went on with red light-green light.

Just as it was my turn to be it, my father came out the door. "Janie," he called. "Come in now. It's getting dark."

I looked up at the sky.

The sun was still up. "No, it isn't,
Dad," I called back.

I saw him turn his head and look up.
He looked at his watch and then at the
sky again. He went back inside the door.

"O.K.," I said, "I'm ready to play."
So we did, for about I-don't-know-how-
long.

People began yawning. Alfred went to sleep under a tree, and Tommy took him home. Mark said his eyes hurt and he was going to go put a cold washcloth on them. Sarah cried when she hit her head, and she said she must be tired. I knew that must be it, because Sarah almost never cried. Jo was getting mad about just little things. Soon no one was left but me.

I looked at the big sun in the sky. It was red now and looked as if it wanted to go down. But it couldn't because of my neverset invention.

I threw the ball up in the air and tried to catch it with one hand.

A cat came along. I ran after it, all the way down the street and back again. Then I gave it some milk in a dish.

I began to kick a rock down the street.

The sun was still up. It was still very light. And I was sick and tired of it.

I ran into the house. I ran past where my father sat yawning over his book and ran right into my closet. I took out my Neverset. I got some pliers. I used the pliers to take out the big nails, and the little nails, and the baseball cards. I took off the yellow and green shirt.

I looked into the can and the golf
ball was there, all right, but it was
now red. Just like the sun.

I took it out, and it was very, very
hot. But I put it in some water and
scrubbed it until all the red was gone.
Then I scrubbed off all the yellow.
Soon it was back to white again. I had
to turn the light on because it was
getting very dark.

I looked out the window just in time
to see the sun going down over the Banners'
roof. "Janie," said my father. "Go to bed
now. It's late."

"It sure is," I whispered.

As I was yawning, I threw away my
neverset invention. It didn't work after all.
Because it's not fun to play kick-the-can
when it's light out.

The Very First

"I want to hit this ball so hard,"
Said the sly and very calm rat.
So he got a board, a saw, and some paint
To invent the very first _____.

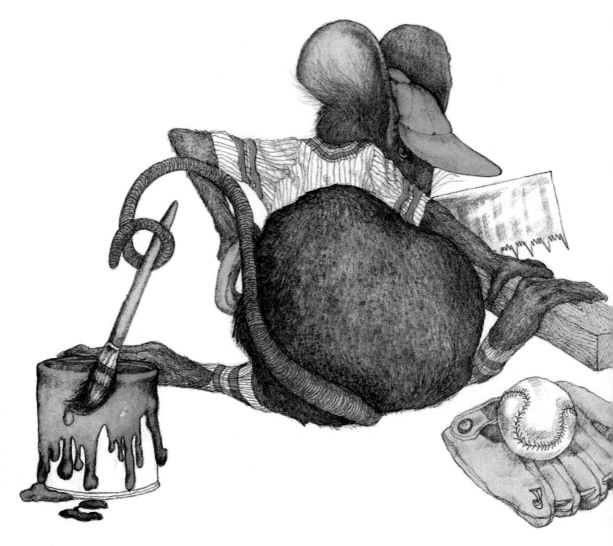

"I want to go across the lake,"
Said the very nice little black goat.
So she got a board and an old orange sheet
To invent the very first _____.

"Today is my birthday, I'm happy to say,"
Said the green and hungry snake.
So he got some flour, eggs, and a bowl
To invent the very first _____.

"When I stand all day, I get so tired,"

Said the jolly and bushy black bear.

So she got a board, a cushion, and nails

To invent the very first _____.

"I want my hair longer and yellow,"

Said the happy and funny big pig.

So she got some hair, some paper, and paste

To invent the very first _____.

The Galloping Goose

We work with words.

animal   zebra   parade

giraffe   ginger   hinge

brought   taught   right

Sound the words.

travel

passengers

galloping

motor

through

railroad

Sight words.

We got some packages.

Our friend lives in the mountains

in Colorado.

The Galloping Goose was not a goose
at all. It was really a train that people
named the Galloping Goose.

A long time ago, there were two small
towns in Colorado that were not very far
from each other. The best way to travel
between the towns was by railroad.

But because the mountains there were
so high, the Galloping Goose had trouble
going between them.

The Galloping Goose was made by two
people. They would collect old parts here
and there. The motor from a car pulled
the train. They used chairs from buses
for the passengers to sit on. A boxcar
was put on the back to carry things.
All this was put on railroad wheels.
Then it could run on the same tracks as
a train.

As the train rolled down the tracks,
it shook and bounced. So the people
named it the Galloping Goose.

After the first Galloping Goose was used, six more were made. Each one had a picture of a goose painted on it.

People made fun of the Galloping Goose, but they still liked it.
Without the train, the people couldn't carry things over the mountains. Food and packages could be loaded in the boxcar at one town. The train would carry the food and packages to the other town.

A ride on the Galloping Goose was fun. Everyone got on the train and sat down in their chairs. The motor, wheels, and boxcar jumped and shook. And the Galloping Goose moved down the tracks.

The train would travel slowly at first. The motor strained and strained as it pulled the loaded boxcar. Slowly, the Galloping Goose moved through the mountains.

Before long the train got to the top of the mountains. The wheels made a funny noise as the train came to a stop. Here the passengers could rest and look around. They could see both of the towns from here. The mountains were very high, so the people could see miles and miles of Colorado land.

Soon it was time to go down the mountain to the other town. As the train went down, it moved faster. It seemed that the Galloping Goose was flying down the tracks.

The train suddenly swayed and bounced around a corner. And the passengers hung on to their chairs. Faster and faster the Galloping Goose went. Soon it got to the town and came to a stop. The people laughed and talked about their fast ride. It was really fun.

Now a highway goes between the towns. The people don't travel by train now, so the railroad had to close down. But the people never forgot their fast ride through the Colorado mountains. A ride on the Galloping Goose was fun.

Where in the World…?

A New Language for Pablo

We work with words.

magic	travel	color
noise	enjoy	point

Sound the words.

United States
Spanish
lonesome
join
understand

Sight words.

<u>Pablo</u> is from <u>Mexico</u>.

But he learned the <u>English</u> <u>language</u>.

Pablo didn't <u>answer</u>.

The New Home

Pablo was a small boy when his family moved from Mexico to the United States. Pablo couldn't speak English. But he could speak Spanish, the language of Mexico.

Pablo liked the town where his family had moved. Best of all he liked the park where the children played. Still, Pablo was lonesome. He sat quietly and watched the other kids play games. He wished he could play games with them. But he couldn't speak their language.

One day he decided to join them. He started to walk over to the other children. He smiled at them.

"Hello," said Gail, "what's your name?"

Pablo didn't understand what she said, so he didn't answer her.

"What's wrong? Can't you talk?" she asked. It was one of her jokes, but Pablo still didn't understand.

The other kids smiled at Pablo, but he didn't know what to do. He wanted to cry, but he knew that wouldn't help. At last, he just decided to go home.

On his way home, Pablo thought and thought. He was very lonesome. He wished he were back in Mexico. There, his friends could speak his language. He saw other children on the street. But he was afraid to look at them. He wished that they could speak Spanish, too. But he knew that they couldn't.

Pablo walked into the house. His mother came over to speak to him.

"Why, Pablo," his mother said quietly in Spanish, "what's wrong? Why are you so lonesome? Don't you like the United States?"

"Yes," Pablo answered in Spanish. "I like it here very much. But the children laugh at me. I can't join them, because I don't speak English."

"Poor Pablo," said his mother. "But you must not be sad. You must learn their language."

It would be hard for Pablo to learn to speak English, but he decided to try.

We work with words.   Sound the words.

                                          studied

author   feather   dollar   color

narrow   button   happen   embarrassed

pride   princess   present   proud

Sight word.

His name is Mr. <u>Vela</u>.

A New Way to Speak

Pablo's mother began to tell him English words she had learned. Pablo studied and studied and studied. He worked hard for weeks.

Soon, he could understand what people said to him, but the English words were hard for him to say.

In a few weeks, school started. Pablo's mother went with him on the first day. She wanted to meet Pablo's new teacher and to see the school.

Pablo knew that some of the children from the park would be in his room. He was afraid they would laugh at him again. Pablo went to his chair and sat quietly.

Pablo went to school each day. He could understand what his teacher, Mr. Vela, said. But for many weeks he sat quietly and never held up his hand.

One day Mr. Vela held up a card.
He said, "Pablo, what color
is this card?"

Pablo was embarrassed. He didn't
know the right English word to say. His
answer came slowly. "Rojo."

"Rojo!" the other children all laughed.
Pablo wanted to cry. He held his head
down because he was so embarrassed.

"Children," said Mr. Vela. "Pablo has told you how to say red in Spanish. Rojo means red. Now, Pablo, how do you say green in Spanish?"

"Verde," answered Pablo with a proud look on his face.

"Verde means green. Now, Pablo, tell us how to say blue."

"Azul," Pablo answered quickly.

"Azul means blue," said Mr. Vela. "Now yellow."

"Amarillo," said Pablo.

"Very good, Pablo," said Mr. Vela. "Now I will show you a card. And you tell us its color in English."

Pablo started to answer slowly, and he said the name of every color.

"You see," said the teacher, "Pablo can do something that we can't do."

Pablo was very proud about showing the others he could speak English.

Mr. Vela smiled, and all the other children smiled, too.

"But Pablo," said Mr. Vela, "we know only one language. Would you help us learn Spanish?"

Pablo smiled. He didn't know what to say, but he was proud.

"Class," said Mr. Vela, "how many of you would like to learn how to speak Spanish?"

When all the kids held up their hands, Pablo knew what to say.

"Yes, I will tell the class all I know about Spanish."

During the next weeks at school Pablo and the other children had fun. They learned to count to ten in Spanish and English. And they learned the color names rojo, verde, azul, and amarillo.

After a while, Pablo didn't feel embarrassed to speak. Soon, he stopped wishing to be back in Mexico. He was happy to be living in the United States.

Think About This:

1. Why did the children laugh at Pablo?
2. What made Pablo happy to be living in the United States?
3. If you didn't speak English, why would it be hard to live in the United States?

No Help At All___

chac

storm

garden

soon   room   cool   loom

beast

The <u>Maya</u> <u>climbed</u> up the tree.

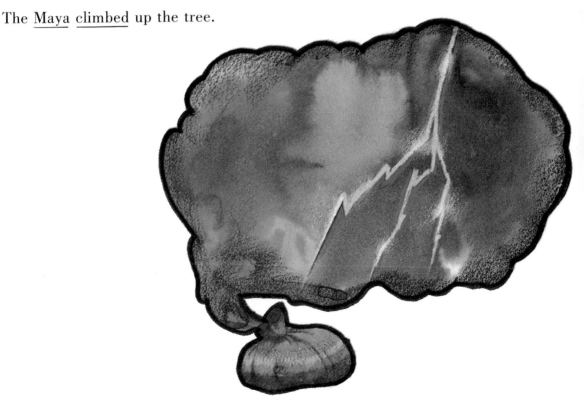

Up to the Clouds

West Chac lived in the sky over the land of Maya. Three other chacs lived in the sky. Each had a house under a big tree. Each had a bag to hold the wind and a pan to hold the rain. And each had a stone ax that made storm clouds.

When the Maya wanted rain, they called to one of the chacs. They gave the chac food. Then they asked him to ride the clouds and spill the rain. But they didn't call to West Chac. "West Rain," said the Maya, "isn't good for corn."

West Chac's house was black. His tree was black and his garden grew black corn.

He had a loom that made black storm clouds. There was a turtle to sit on or to hold down the loom, and a magic pan that cooked his food.

Frogs and toads were his friends. They liked to sing with him, but West Chac had no time.

No one asked him to spill the rain.
No one gave him food. So West Chac
had to work in his garden all the time.
Sometimes in winter he rode the clouds
and let some of the wind out of his bag.
But in the summer he had the garden
to care for.

He didn't even have time to sit on
the turtle and sing with his friends.

"I must have help," he said. But
the other chacs had work to do, too.

One day West Chac was pulling up a yam when he heard, "Help! Help!" He pulled up another yam and looked under it. Down below, a boy climbed a tree. He climbed to get away from a hungry beast. But the beast climbed the tree, too.

"Help!" said the boy. "Someone help me!"

West Chac said, "If I help you, then you must help me."

"For how long?" asked the boy.

"For as long as I say."

"That could be always," said the boy.

"Yes, it could," said West Chac.

The boy said, "No." Then he said,
"Ow, ow, ow! Yes! I will help you for
as long as you say. Just get me away
from this hungry beast!"

West Chac put down a rope. The rope
grew until the boy took it. West Chac
pulled him up. "Now," said the chac,
"you can help me."

"No," said the boy. "Now I must eat."

West Chac told him, "Go into the house.
Tell the pan to give you a corn cake."

The boy thought, "I can eat more than
one corn cake." He told the pan, "Give me a
lot of corn cake." And the pan did.

"Help! Help!" said the boy.

West Chac had to run and stop the
pan. "That did not help me," he said.
"It made more to do."

"I will clean the house," said the boy.

"Good," said West Chac. "I will ask my friends to eat and sing with me."

The boy went in to clean the house. He put down new mats and took away the old mats. When he came back, there were a lot of frogs and toads in the house. "Get out!" he told them. They did not want to go, but he made them get out.

"Where are my friends?" asked West Chac.

The boy said, "No one was here, just a lot of toads and frogs in the clean house. It took a long time to get them all out."

"You put out my friends," said
West Chac. "What kind of help is that?"

"But I did clean the house,"
said the boy.

"Well, I must have help in the
garden," said West Chac. "Can you cut
down trees? I need a new corn field."

"I can cut trees if you give me a
stone ax," said the boy.

West Chac told him, "Cut only the
little trees."

The boy thought, "With a stone ax,
I can cut big trees." He cut the biggest
tree of all. It began to fall. "Help!"
he said.

nine

yams

bushy   bullet   pushing   pull

helping

house   ground   towel   cloud

Back Home

West Chac ran to help the boy. The
tree cut the boy into nine parts. Nine
times the chac sang, and the nine
parts went back together. "You are not
much help with trees," said the chac.
"Can you dig yams?"

"Oh, yes," said the boy. "I can pull
up yams."

West Chac told him, "Just dig the
yams. Don't look under them."

But the boy did look under the yams,
and he saw his mother and father. He
wanted to go home, so he got the chac's
rope and climbed down it.

But the rope did not grow longer,
as it had done before. "Help! Help!
Pull me up!" said the boy.

West Chac had to run and pull him up.

"I am always helping you," he said.
"When will you start helping me?"

The boy said, "Maybe you should let me go home."

"No," said the chac, "I must have help."

But the boy thought only of home and how to get there. He took a black cloud from the loom and the bag of wind to make it fly. But he couldn't hold the bag shut. And the wind got out. "Help! He-e-e-lp!" he called.

West Chac ran and got the wind. He put it back in the bag. He made the cloud stop, and he pulled the boy back to the garden. "You are no help at all," said the chac. He pulled up a yam and put down the rope and made the boy go home.

At home all the trees were down.

"That was the biggest wind I ever saw," said Mother. "Even the duck blew away."

"I will have a big corn field now," said Father.

The boy said, "I did that! I made a place for the new corn field!" And he told them everything.

His father and mother gave West Chac a lot of things for helping the boy. When the corn was ready to grow and people called the chacs, they gave West Chac something to keep his wind bag shut.

Then West Chac had time to sit on
the turtle and sing with his friends.
"That boy was some help after all,"
he said.

Hummingbird

Sound the words.

Hummingbird

captured

dough   snow   bowl   though

glove   honey   done   none

Sight words.

Little <u>Wolf</u> got to ride in an <u>Indian</u> <u>canoe</u>.

It was a <u>special</u> canoe.

Long ago, before the United States got
its name, there lived a Nootka Indian
girl named Hummingbird. This was her
name because when she was one day old,
her brother, Leaping Deer, captured his
first hummingbird. After he captured
the bird, Leaping Deer danced, even as
Hummingbird gave her first cry.
Even though other Nootka children had
captured the small, fast birds, none
seemed as special as this one. Everyone
knew that Hummingbird got her name in a
special way.

Hummingbird was a happy little girl. She didn't mind the name Hummingbird until she started to play with the shell. That is when Hummingbird knew that she was small for her age.

Bear Face would throw a shell down the beach. Then the other Nootka children would run and try to be the first to pick the shell up. They would run as fast as they could. But Hummingbird couldn't keep up with the others. Even those who were not her age were faster. She was smaller than all the other Indian children.

Leaping Deer said, "It is because of me that you are so well named, my sister. You are as small as a Hummingbird."

Bear Face laughed and said, "She is as small, but not as fast."

"What good is such a little bird?" thought Hummingbird. "What good am I?"

Hummingbird was happy when the family got a new baby brother. They called him Little Wolf. She would look after Little Wolf and do special things for him. She was glad that there was someone in the family smaller than she was.

In time, Little Wolf grew as tall as Hummingbird, though they were not the same age. And even though Hummingbird was older than most of her friends, she was still smaller than any of them.

Soon Little Wolf could play games with the older Nootka children. The children would make two teams. And the teams would stand across from each other in a line. Then they looked at each other and said funny things, until someone on the other team smiled.

One day, both teams were doing well. Then Bear Face said, "Little Wolf will go on the great hunt and catch the biggest whale!" That was the end of the game, because Little Wolf smiled. The other team won.

In a few days, it was time for the great whale hunt. The people worked hard to get each large, carved canoe ready. Hummingbird stood on the beach.

She looked at each beautiful, carved canoe and felt proud. She knew that the carved canoe of her father was the most beautiful one.

The hunters would be gone for days on this great hunt.

When they had left, Leaping Deer said, "Let's go, Hummingbird. We have much work to do. Come, Little Wolf."

But where was Little Wolf?

Suddenly Hummingbird began to jump up and down on the beach. She was shouting at the hunters. "Come back!"

But the hunters could not see her. Now she began to beat the drum. Leaping Deer thought she must have gone mad. His father would be very angry.

Leaping Deer saw the canoe of his father come back. What had Hummingbird done?

He saw his father in the canoe. But what did he have in his hands? Leaping Deer looked hard. Soon he could see what it was.

It was Little Wolf!

He had been hiding in the canoe. But why?

The canoe came in. Hummingbird's father said to her, "How did you know your little brother was in my canoe?"

"We were playing a game," answered the girl. "Bear Face said something to Little Wolf. He said Little Wolf would go on the next whale hunt and catch the biggest whale."

"But I only wanted to make him laugh," said Bear Face.

"You did make him laugh," said Hummingbird. "But only because he thought you were right!"

"You are small, my sister," said
Leaping Deer. "But you think as quickly
as a hummingbird can fly. And it is
because of me that you are so well
named."

Bear Face and all the others knew he
was right. None of her friends would
laugh at her again.

Now Hummingbird felt as big as the
whale. She would always be called
Hummingbird, but now she was happy and
proud of the name.

Under the Cherry Tree

We work with words.

care   bare   share

paper   final   notion

Sound the words.

glared

Japan

miserly

raise

month

cherry

mumbled

collecting

Sight words.

The landlord went to the <u>village</u>.

He said "<u>Bah</u>!" to all the <u>villagers</u>.

The Mean Old Landlord

There once lived an old landlord in a small village in Japan. He lived all alone in a big house. All the land and every house for miles around was his. And he was so mean babies cried when they saw him.

He was so miserly he never took a bath, so he could save water. He was so mean he would raise the rent in the village month after month until the villagers were very, very poor.

But even in a poor village, spring is a beautiful time. There are baby birds all around, and the cherry trees bloom all at once.

"It's spring again. I can tell by all the noise the birds make. Bah!" said the old man.

On one day like this, the villagers took what food they had and went out to a beautiful field to eat under the cherry trees. They ate and sang and danced the time away. It was the best day of the year.

The miserly landlord went out to the field, too. He took a bag of cherries and sat under a cherry tree all alone. As he popped one cherry after another into his mouth, he mumbled and grumbled and glared at his neighbors.

"Hmm, look at them dance. That's all they ever do, dance and eat, eat and dance. They're just like children. Why are they so happy? Bah!"

Then, just by chance, he ate a cherry pit. His face changed to red, blue, and then green. The cherry pit bounced around and around inside him until it got to the top of his head. There it came to rest.

When the mean landlord got up the next morning, he could feel something growing from the top of his head. It was a cherry tree.

"Hmm, what's this? A tree? Now what will I do with my hat? Bah!"

He was too miserly to see a doctor and
too mean to worry about it. So he went
around collecting rent with a cherry
tree growing out of the top of his head.

A lot of rain and the warm summer
wind made the tree grow quickly.

"The tree must think my head is a garden," said the mean old landlord. "Bah!"

The tree grew and grew. The next spring it began to bloom. The best day of the year had come around once again.

The villagers had very little money, but they had saved month after month for this day. They ate and sang and danced the time away and sat around the landlord to look at his tree.

"What beautiful flowers!"

"How does he make it grow?"

"Money, more than likely."

The miserly landlord was very angry. He mumbled and grumbled and glared at the people. "Don't you ever make fun of me!" he said. "You won't get away with this! I'll raise your rent first thing in the morning. See how you like that! Look at you, dance and eat, eat and dance. That's all you ever do. Look at your children. They are fat! You're no better. And you make fun of me! I'll get you!"

The landlord took hold of the tree
trunk with both hands, and with one fast
tug, pulled the beautiful tree out of
his head.

"He's gone mad!" the villagers began shouting.

"He is mad!"

"Run for it, everyone!"

The people had never seen their landlord so angry. They quickly took their children and ran home.

The next morning the landlord found a large hole in the top of his head.

"Hmm . . . a hole, and it's empty," he said. "So that's why my head felt so light last night."

He had never once gone to a doctor, and he was not about to start now. So he went around collecting rent with a large hole in the top of his head.

Think About This:

1. Why do you think the landlord in this story is so mean?

2. The landlord in this story is mean. Why, then, do you think the villagers were still so happy in the spring?

Fish in a Puddle

Summer soon came to the village, and with summer came much rain.

It didn't take the rain long to fill the hole in the landlord's head with water.

"Water in my head!" said the landlord. "Bah! A puddle is only good for children and bugs! Now I'll have to sleep sitting up. If I don't, there will be a puddle of water all over my bed. Trouble, trouble, trouble. Bah!"

But in place of bugs, fish began to swim in the hole on top of his head. As it happened, the fish got big, and the old landlord was kind of happy about that.

"Since I have fish in my head, I won't have to go to the store for fish," said the miserly old man. "I have saved more money!"

The landlord liked to take a nap during the day. He always sat up to be sure to keep every one of his fish in his head. When the landlord took his nap, it was a nice time of day for the villagers. That was the only time the old landlord was not mean.

Tabo, a boy in the town, happened to see the fish that jumped out of the puddle in the landlord's head. One day after school, Tabo scrambled up to the landlord's house. The second the old man began to sleep, Tabo got his friends. They all went up to the landlord's house.

"Let's get some fish from the landlord's head while he takes a nap," he whispered.

The children took care not to catch their hooks on the landlord's ears. And they were very quiet as they put their hooks down in the water in the landlord's head. Each day the children would fish in the landlord's head. They wanted to catch one of his beautiful big fish.

One day, Tabo got the biggest fish on his hook the children ever saw. The great fish jumped out of the mean man's head and shook him out of his sleep.

"What's this! Water! Cold water! Oh! It's my fish!"

Shouting, he jumped up. "You boys! Don't you ever take my fish!"

The landlord ran into the valley after the boys. He was so mad he didn't see a rock, and he fell right over it.

"Ow!" cried the landlord.

Then everything happened at once.
The landlord went flying into the air.
His legs went into the hole in his head,
and suddenly the old man was gone!
All that was left of the landlord was a
beautiful lake in the valley.

When the children came out from behind the trees, they saw fish in the deep clean water.

"Look at those beautiful fish," cried Tabo. The children ran home and told everyone.

When the villagers heard what had happened, they were very happy. They went to the lake and sang and danced their time away. There were birds all around and the cherry trees were in bloom all at once.

And before long, the lake came to be known as the best place in the valley.

Think About This:

1. Why did the landlord sleep sitting up?
2. What happened to the landlord when he fell over the rock?
3. Why do you think the lake became the best place in the valley?

Who can stay indoors
on such a day with the sun
dazzling on new snow!

Kikaku

A full moon comes up,
and stars, stars uncountable,
drown in a green sky.

Shiki

Shhhhhh!

Are You a Good Witness?

We work with words.

cry   crate   crack

surprised   mistake   center

Sound the words.

crime

arrive

witness

Sight word.

Did you <u>notice</u> what time it was?

Here you are at the scene of the crime. Soon the police will arrive. They will want to talk to a witness. A witness is someone who sees a crime and can remember it. Do you think you can do it?

Look at the picture on the next page for a little while. See if you can remember everything in the picture — the people and the things you see.

Be sure to notice everything. You may remember there is a clock. But did you notice the time?

After you look at the picture, turn the page. On page 222 you can see how much you can remember. Before you look back at the picture of the crime, think very hard about what you saw.

Ready? Go!

What time does the clock say?

What day is it?

How many crooks are in the room?

Is there someone else around?

How did the crooks get into the room?

What do the crooks want to do?

Is there a fire in the room?

Are there any plants in the room?

What was cut on the table?

Does one crook have on a hat?

Have they knocked anything over when coming into the house?

Turn back the page to look at the picture again.

Are you a good witness?

Would you be ready when the police arrive?

Be a Good Detective

We work with words.

number	collar	major
class	claim	cloth
carry	arrow	shallow

Sound the words.

fingerprints

towel

finger

middle

clue

follow

Sight word.

I use my <u>thumb</u> when I write.

How to Read Fingerprints

First you have to get some
fingerprints to read. Use an ink pad
and a paper towel. You will use the
towel to clean your fingers. Make cards
like the one here. The fingerprints
will go in the little boxes on the cards.

Try to take your own fingerprints first. Put one finger on the ink pad. Keep it on the pad, but roll it from left to right. Then put your finger in its space on one of the cards. Roll it the same way, from left to right. Then lift your finger with care so that the ink doesn't smudge. If the ink does smudge, the fingerprint will not show each line of your finger. Now clean your finger with the paper towel.

Make a fingerprint of each finger. There is a space on the cards for your thumb, pointer finger, middle finger, ring finger, and little finger on each hand.

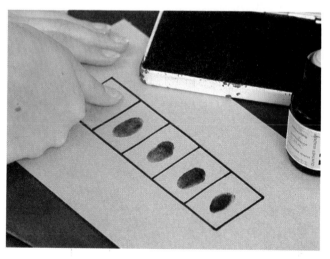

No two people have the same fingerprints, you know. That's why a fingerprint is a good clue to who was at the scene of a crime. Here are three kinds of fingerprints to look for.

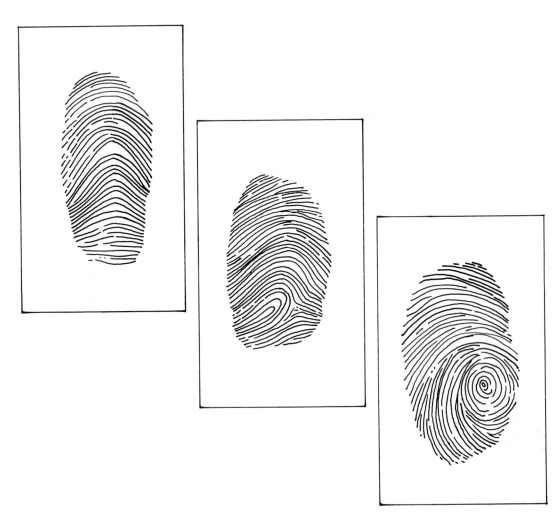

Does one picture look like your fingerprints?

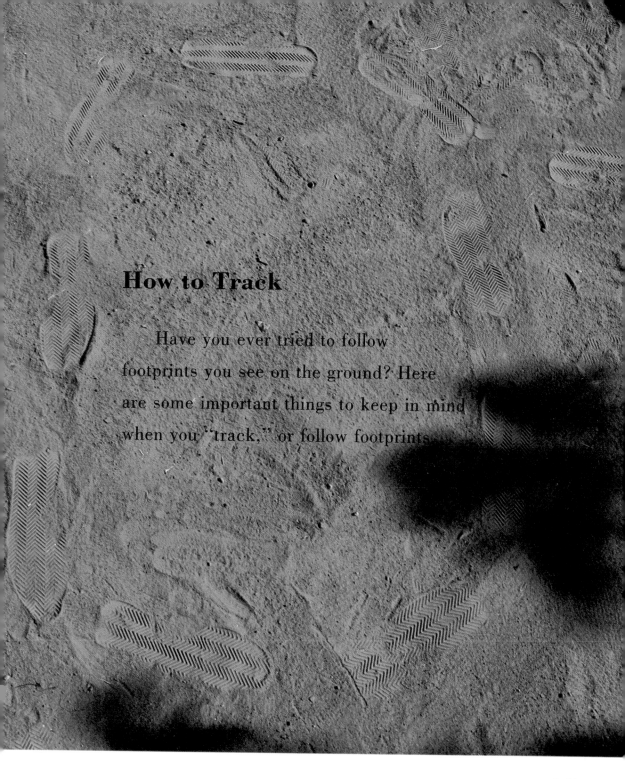

How to Track

Have you ever tried to follow
footprints you see on the ground? Here
are some important things to keep in mind
when you "track," or follow footprints.

1. Don't look just at the footprints. Look all around. You don't want to miss an important clue.

2. The trail sometimes leads to hard ground. Then the footprints will not show up. See if rocks or grass on the trail give a clue to where the person or animal went. You can then try to stay on the trail until you can see the footprints again.

3. You can sometimes tell how old footprints are. See if there is water in them. If so, they were made before the last rain. See if a lot of grass or little branches are in the middle of them. If so, they were made before a day when there was a lot of wind.

4. You can tell things about the person who made the footprints, too.

See if the footprints are not as close together as they were at the first part of the trail. If so, you know that the person started to run.

5. If the footprints face the other way, the person wanted to turn around. Maybe he wanted to turn around to see if someone tried to follow him. If the person has a funny kind of walk, this will show up in the footprints, too.

6. What if you have lost the trail? You
can mark your place with a stick. This way,
you can remember where you have been. Then
you can look around for another clue.

The Owl Tape

We work with words.

guess	guilt	guitar
dirty	funny	noise

Sound the words.

guys

robbery

bank

somewhere

horned

The Owl Hunters

Kevin and Mark bounced a ball back and forth and talked about the robbery at their town bank.

"Do you think he'll get away with the robbery?" asked Kevin.

"No way," Mark said. "The police shut everything off quickly. He's probably hiding somewhere close by, afraid to run."

"That's almost funny," Kevin said. "All that money and nothing to do but sit on it. Hey," he said suddenly, "isn't that Toby over there?"

Someone ran into the woods down the road and seemed to be hiding.

"It looks like Toby," Mark said. "But I don't think he wants us to see him. Let's see what he's doing."

The boys ran after Toby.

"Hey, Bird Man, what are you doing?" Kevin said. "Aren't you afraid the bank robber will get you—all alone here in the woods?"

Everyone called Toby Bird Man because he liked to study birds so much.

Toby got tired of being called Bird Man, but he put up with it because he didn't want to give up his bird study.

"Come on, guys," said Toby. "Leave me alone. I've got something to do, and it'll be dark soon."

The boys followed Toby into the woods.

"Did you guys know there's a great horned owl in these woods?" Toby asked.

"Are they good to eat?" Kevin asked. Mark laughed.

"Oh, come on," said Toby. "I knew it lived in here somewhere, and the other day, I found its tree. It's way back in the woods where no one ever goes."

"Why are you going now?" asked Mark. "It'll be too dark to see much."

"I know. But I want to set up my tape recorder and try to get its call," said Toby. "I don't have a tape of a great horned owl yet. Look, there's the tree."

Toby put the recorder up in the branches of the tree.

"Let's go," he said. "It's not dark yet, so the owl is still up there."

Suddenly Mark threw the ball into the branches and called, "Come on, owl, get up!"

There was a loud, loud noise. The branches shook and shook, and the great horned owl went flying through the night air.

Toby glared at Mark. "I knew you guys would blow everything," he said. "Now you can see why I was hiding from you."

The Owl and the Robber

The next day, when Toby answered the door, he was surprised to find Mark there.

"Now what?" he asked.

"Look, Bird Man, I mean Toby," Mark
said. "I thought a lot about what I
did to you and I'm sorry. I thought I
was being funny, but I was just being
mean."

"O.K.," said Toby. "Hey, why don't
you come in? I want you to hear
something."

Mark followed Toby to his bedroom.
He said, "You mean you got the owl call
on tape?"

"No, not the call. This is something
else."

"Really mysterious?" Mark asked.

"Well, it's mysterious to me, that's for sure," said Toby.

He pushed a button and the tape came on. At first they heard sounds you would hear in the woods. But then they heard footsteps and a lot of other strange sounds.

"Footsteps," whispered Mark. "Did you go back there, Toby?"

"Only after the tape was made," said Toby.

Mark went on with his questions. "Could an animal make noises like that?"

"I don't think so," Toby said. "I bet it's the robber! We can find him and get a reward."

"No way," Mark said. "The police picked up the robber this morning. They didn't get the money back yet, but they will."

"Oh, well," said Toby. "I guess we won't get any reward money."

As Mark walked home, he thought and thought about the noises on the tape. Quickly, he ran to see Kevin.

Kevin was on the front porch when Mark got to his house.

Kevin could tell something was going on.

"Come on! Let's go!" Mark called.

"Hey, what's wrong?" asked Kevin.

"Don't ask any questions," said Mark. "I'll tell you on the way."

As they ran through the woods, Mark told Kevin about the tape.

"I think," Mark said, "that the robber hid the money by the owl tree. The noises on the tape were the robber walking and hiding the money! If we can get the money back, we'll get a reward. I'd like to give it to Toby, since I made the owl fly off."

"That would be nice of you," said Kevin.

Just then they came to the tree. There stood the robber with the money. He had just gotten it from its hiding place.

"So the police got the wrong man!" whispered Mark.

But before anyone could move, there was a loud noise up in the tree. And something large fell down, right on the robber.

It was Toby! He was sitting on
the robber, and the robber was out cold.

"You guys sure took your time! I
thought I was going to be up in that
tree all night!" said Toby.

"What were you doing up there?"
asked Mark and Kevin at the same time.

"I was up in the tree, trying to tape
the owl, when the robber came. I
had to sit still and not make any noise.
But then the owl started to fly off,
and I fell," Toby said.

"Are you O.K.?" asked Kevin.

"Sure," said Toby. "But someone
better get the police before the robber
gets up. I'm sure they have some
questions to ask him."

Glossary

A a

airline (air line)
People fly in planes that are owned by an *airline*.

amarillo (a ma ri llo)
The Spanish word for "yellow" is *amarillo*.

anthill (ant hill)
Ants build a home in the ground called an *anthill*.

arrow (ar row)
A hunter of long ago used a bow and *arrow*.

azul (a zul)
The Spanish word for "blue" is *azul*.

B b

banish (ban ish)
The king could send away, or *banish*, a person to another country.

beast (beast)
A large animal is sometimes called a *beast*.

bloom (bloom)
When apple trees *bloom*, their branches have many beautiful flowers.

bow (bow)
1. Arrows are shot with a *bow*.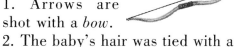
2. The baby's hair was tied with a pretty yellow *bow*.

boxcar (box car)
A train car with closed sides and a roof is a *boxcar*.

brook (brook)
The water in the *brook* was not deep.

building (build ing)
They are *building* a house with wood and nails.

bushy (bush y)
This dog has a *bushy* tail, but an elephant does not.

C c

canoe (ca noe)
A small boat that is pointed at both ends is a *canoe*.

carved (carved)
This beautiful wood box has been *carved*.

case (case)
1. The detective was working on a robbery *case*.
2. This box is a *case* of peaches.

cast (cast)
1. They *cast* the fishing line into the water.

2. All the people who act in a play are the *cast*.
3. A broken leg must be put in a *cast*.

cattle (cat tle)
They bought ten more cows so they would have more *cattle*.

chac (chac)
Some people believe that an important being called a *chac* brings rain.

chimpanzee (chim pan zee)
An ape that lives in trees and has big ears is a *chimpanzee*.

chuck (chuck)
They loaded the food in a *chuck* wagon.

closet (clos et)
A small room for storing clothes is a *closet*.

club (club)
1. A big stick made of wood or metal is a *club*.

2. Many people make friends and have fun in this *club*.

clump (clump)
1. The bushes were planted together in a *clump*.
2. That loud noise is the *clump* of their boots on the porch.

Colorado (Col o ra do)
A state known for its mountains is *Colorado*.

crate (crate)
A wooden box for packing things is a *crate*.

cricket (crick et)
1. A large bug that makes a strange noise is a *cricket*.

2. Baseball is a little like the English game *cricket*.

crook
1. Someone could sit in the *crook* of that tree branch.
2. Another name for a robber is *crook*.

curb (curb)
The raised stone along the side of the street is the *curb*.

cushion (cush ion)
That chair is hard, but this chair has a good *cushion*.

D d

detective (de tec tive)
That important clue and the fingerprints were found by a *detective*.

dough (dough)
A mixture of flour, eggs, water, and milk is *dough*.

dragon (drag on)
A make-believe animal that has wings and blows fire is a *dragon*.

E e

ear (ear)
1. People and animals hear through each *ear*.
2. The part of a corn plant that we eat is the *ear*.

elephant (el e phant)
A large animal with a long trunk is an *elephant*.

F f

fingerprints (fin ger prints)
The robber left a trail of *fingerprints*.

fireplace (fire place)
We were very cold, so we built a fire in the *fireplace*.

flour (flour)
The ground wheat used to make bread is *flour*.

G g

galloping (gal lop ing)
That horse is *galloping* very fast.

giant (gi ant)
A very large person or animal is a *giant*.

giraffe (gi raffe)
An animal with a long neck and long legs is a *giraffe*.

gloomy (gloom y)
They looked out at the rain with *gloomy* faces.

glove (glove)
My hand is kept warm or kept from harm by a *glove*.

goldenrod (gold en rod)
In late summer, the small, yellow flower called *goldenrod* begins to bloom.

golf (golf)
An outdoor game played with clubs and small, hard balls is *golf*.

groundhog (ground hog)
A fat little animal that sleeps all winter is the *groundhog*.

H h

helicopter (hel i cop ter)
That flying machine with no wings is a *helicopter*.

hiding (hid ing)
They never knew I was there because I was *hiding*.

high-heeled (high heeled)
They looked tall in their *high-heeled* boots.

highway (high way)
We drive to the city on a *highway*.

horned (horned)
Some deer, sheep, and cattle are *horned* animals.

hospital (hos pi tal)
Sick people are taken care of in a *hospital*.

hummingbird (hum ming bird)
A small bird that moves its wings very fast is the *hummingbird*.

J j

Japan (Ja pan)
The sea is all around the country of *Japan*.

jeep (jeep)
She drove across the field in her *jeep*.

K k

kettle (ket tle)
The water was heated in a *kettle* on the stove.

L l

lamb (lamb)
A baby sheep is called a *lamb*.

loom (loom)
1. Cloth is made on a *loom*.
2. The giant bears *loom* over the little rabbits.

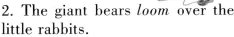

M m

machines (ma chines)
A car, a truck, and a loom are *machines*.

mailbox (mail box)
The mail carrier puts mail in a *mailbox*.

market (mar ket)
People sell things at a *market*.

Mexico (Mex i co)
A country where many people speak Spanish is *Mexico*.

morning (morn ing)
The sun comes up in the *morning*.

motor (mo tor)
A car is run by a *motor*.

N n

newspaper (news pa per)
They read about the robbery in the *newspaper*.

noodles (noo dles)
The cook put egg *noodles* in the vegetable soup.

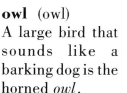

O o

orange (or ange)
1. A round, reddish-yellow fruit is an *orange*.
2. Sometimes the sun looks reddish yellow, or *orange*.

owl (owl)
A large bird that sounds like a barking dog is the horned *owl*.

P p

packages (pack ag es)
We put the clothes in boxes and then mailed the *packages*.

palace (pal ace)
The home of the king and queen is in a beautiful *palace*.

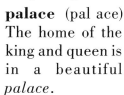

passengers (pas sen gers)
People who ride in cars but do not drive are *passengers*.

pasture (pas ture)
Cows ate the grass in the *pasture*.

pelts (pelts)
1. The coats of animals are called *pelts*.

2. The funny chimpanzee *pelts* a friend with food.

pen (pen)
1. The pet rabbits live in a *pen*.

2. A person can write with a *pen*.

photo (pho to)
This picture in the newspaper is a *photo*.

pit (pit)
1. They will dig a deep *pit* in the ground.
2. In the center of a peach is a *pit*.

plane (plane)
A person can fly in a *plane*.

pliers (pli ers)
A tool for holding or cutting things is *pliers*.

plum (plum)
A red fruit with a pit is a *plum*.

police (po lice)
When they are away, their house is watched by the *police*.

popcorn (pop corn)
A special kind of corn that pops when it is hot is *popcorn*.

puddle (pud dle)
The water in the *puddle* looked brown.

R r

ranger (rang er)
This large park is cared for by a *ranger*.

recorder (re cord er)
This machine, called a tape *recorder*, can keep the sounds of our voices.

reward (re ward)
Money given for finding a robber is a *reward*.

rojo (ro jo)
The Spanish word for "red" is *rojo*.

S s

saw (saw)
1. Wood is cut with a tool called a *saw*.
2. Last week I *saw* a baseball game.

secret (se cret)
Something not to be told to everyone is called a *secret*.

skunk (skunk)
A black-and-white animal known for its bad smell is a *skunk*.

smudge (smudge)
Water can *smudge* the ink on a paper.

stickball (stick ball)
A game something like baseball is *stickball*.

storm (storm)
When the sky gets black and wind blows, a *storm* is coming.

T t

thirty (thir ty)
Three tens is equal to *thirty*.

thumb (thumb)
I have four fingers and a *thumb*.

train (train)
1. Passengers rode from town to town on a *train*.
2. We can *train* a dog to do tricks.

trunk (trunk)
1. This tree has a large *trunk* and many branches.
2. An elephant's nose is called a *trunk*.
3. They put the coats and boots in a *trunk*.

U u

United States (U nit ed States)
There are 50 states, the District of Columbia, and Puerto Rico in the *United States*.

upstairs (up stairs)
The part of a house above the ground floor is *upstairs*.

V v

valley (val ley)
A road runs through the *valley* between the hills.

vegetables (veg e ta bles)
Corn and potatoes are *vegetables*.

verde (ver de)
The Spanish word for "green" is *verde*.

village (village)
A town is bigger than a *village*.

W w

washcloth (wash cloth)
We cleaned the baby's face with a *washcloth*.

whale (whale)
A large animal that swims in the sea is a *whale*.

wolf (wolf)
A wild animal that looks like a dog is a *wolf*.

Y y

yams (yams)
Vegetables that look like orange potatoes are *yams*.

yawning (yawn ing)
When people get sleepy, they start *yawning*.

Z z

zebra (ze bra)
A black-and-white animal that looks like a horse is a *zebra*.

zookeeper (zoo keep er)
The person who cares for animals in a zoo is a *zookeeper*.

ACKNOWLEDGMENTS

Grateful acknowledgment is given for permission to reprint the following copyrighted material:

"Ants Live Here" by Lilian Moore, copyright © 1967 by Lilian Moore, from *I Feel the Same Way*. Used by permission of Atheneum Publishers.

"Are You a Good Witness?" © 1978 Children's Television Workshop. Reprinted with permission from Children's Television Workshop.

"A Bath for Gail Goose" by Miriam Clark Potter, adapted from the book *Mrs. Goose and Three-Ducks* by Miriam Clark Potter, copyright 1936, © renewed 1964 by Miriam Clark Potter. Reprinted by permission of J. B. Lippincott Company.

"Duchess" from *Jack and Jill* magazine, copyright © 1962 by The Curtis Publishing Company. Used by permission of the publisher.

"A Full Moon Comes Up" from *More Cricket Songs: Japanese Haiku*, translated and © 1971 by Harry Behn. Reprinted by permission of Harcourt Brace Jovanovich, Inc., and Curtis Brown, Ltd.

"The Galloping Goose" by Agnes M. Pharo, reprinted by permission of the author and courtesy of *Wee Wisdom* magazine.

"A Groundhog by the Fireplace" from *Jack and Jill* magazine, copyright © 1963 by The Curtis Publishing Company. Used by permission of the publisher.

"How to Read Fingerprints" © 1978 Grosset & Dunlap, Inc. Reprinted with permission from Children's Television Workshop and Grosset & Dunlap, Inc.

"How to Track" © 1978 Grosset & Dunlap, Inc. Reprinted with permission from Children's Television Workshop and Grosset & Dunlap, Inc.

"Hummingbird" from "How Hummingbird Earned Her Name" by Dee Lillegard. Permission granted by the author. Originally published in *Wee Wisdom* magazine, November 1974.

"The King and the Cook" from *Jack and Jill* magazine, copyright © 1962 by The Curtis Publishing Company. Used by permission of the publisher.

"Mr. Ant and the Mistake" from *Jack and Jill* magazine, copyright © 1962 by The Curtis Publishing Company. Used by permission of the publisher.

"Mr. McBean's Train" by Helen King Marple, adapted from "The Little Train That Helped" by Helen King Marple, by permission of Hara-Lou Marple Ratay.

"Mother Skunk's Moving Day" by Mary Peacock, adapted from *Jack and Jill* magazine, copyright © 1964 by The Curtis Publishing Company. Reprinted by permission of the author.

"The Neverset Invention" by Nancy Garber, reprinted by permission of the author and courtesy of *Wee Wisdom* magazine.

"A New Language for Pablo" adapted from "The Boy Who Could Speak Two Languages" from *Jack and Jill* magazine, copyright © 1963 by The Curtis Publishing Company. Used by permission of the publisher.

"No Help at All" by Betty Baker, adaptation of *No Help at All* (text only) by Betty Baker. Text copyright © 1978 by Betty Baker. By permission of Greenwillow Books (A Division of William Morrow & Company) and Curtis Brown, Ltd.

"The Owl Tape" from *Young World* magazine, copyright © 1977 by The Saturday Evening Post Company, Indianapolis, Indiana. Used by permission of the publisher.

"The Popcorn Dragon" by Jane Thayer, (new) adaptation of *The Popcorn Dragon* (text only) by Jane Thayer, copyright 1953 by William Morrow & Company, Inc. By permission of the publisher.

"Runaway Tillie" adapted from "Tillie Runs Away" by Don Lang, *Story Parade*, copyright 1940, renewed 1968 by Story Parade, Inc. Every effort has been made to contact the heirs of Mr. Lang for permission to use "Tillie Runs Away."

"Tom Goldenrod" from "The Hero" by Lawrence J. Epstein, adapted from *Jack and Jill* magazine, © 1977 by The Saturday Evening Post Company, Indianapolis, Indiana. Used by permission of the publisher.